STARTING LINEUP

STATE CHAMPIONS

The Danville Digits are ready for their 100th basketball game. Can you pick out the five starting players? They are the players whose jersey numbers add up to 100.

45

17

10

72

38

9

59

25

29

64

18

8

Hint on page 46

Illustration: Jerry Zimmerman

Answer on page 48

COUNT ON LIZ

You can always count on Liz to have the best parties. This time she's organized a scavenger hunt.

1 cake
2 straws
3 cats
4 birthday cards
5 balloons
6 gift boxes
7 cups
8 noisemakers
9 lollipops
10 party hats
11 candles
12 balls
13 cupcakes
14 crayons

Can you find all the items on the list?

Answer on page 48

5

RIDDLE SQUARES

These squares contain the answers to two different riddles. To find them, look for the number that matches the answer to each clue. Write the letter shown in the square with the matching number on the line next to the clue. When the lines are filled in, read the letters from top to bottom to answer each riddle.

1. What breaks without falling?

ABC on a telephone dial _____

Wonders of the ancient world _____

Months in a season _____

2. What falls without breaking?

Nothing _____

Ones on a clock _____

Half a dozen _____

Quarts in two gallons _____

Ounces in a pound _____

7	0	5
A	N	I
2	4	6
D	E	G
3	8	16
Y	H	T

Answer on page 48

Hint on page 46

Illustration: Vilma Ortiz-Dillon

FINISH BY 5

Hint on page 46

Can you find a path from START to FINISH? You must count upward in order by 5s until you reach 40 at the FINISH. You can't go to a lesser number or to the same number twice.

FINISH
40

25

20

20

25

35

25

35

30

30

25

20

15

20

10   20

20

25

15   15

START 5   10   15

CLOCK WATCHER

A time is printed below each blank space. Find that time on one of the clocks pictured here. Write the letter

Answer on page 48

Hint on page 46

Illustration: Frank Bolle

on that clock into the space
above the matching time.
Take your time as you try to
find the answers to two riddles.

1. What time is everyone's favorite?

___ ___ ___ ___   ___ ___ ___
3:05 2:15 7:30 3:09   7:55 12:45 12:45

**2. How do you know when a clock
is embarrassed?**

___ ___   ___ ___ ___ ___ ___
2:15 3:05   3:45 2:15 6:23 3:09 9:25

___ ___ ___   ___ ___ ___ ___
2:15 3:05 9:25   12:45 12:30 5:23 3:09

___ ___ ___ ___ ___ ___   ___ ___ ___
10:45 3:09 3:45 2:15 1:15 6:23   2:15 3:05 9:25

___ ___ ___ ___ ___
3:45 12:30 1:15 6:23 9:25

9

SPLIT DECISIONS

The Math Makers Club is having its annual bake sale. The members are giving away a free slice of cake to anyone who can identify the shaded fraction amount of each dessert.

Hint on page 46

Illustration: Jason Thorne

Answer on page 48

DOTS A LOT

Answer on page 48

Join the dots in numerical order to find a moving picture.

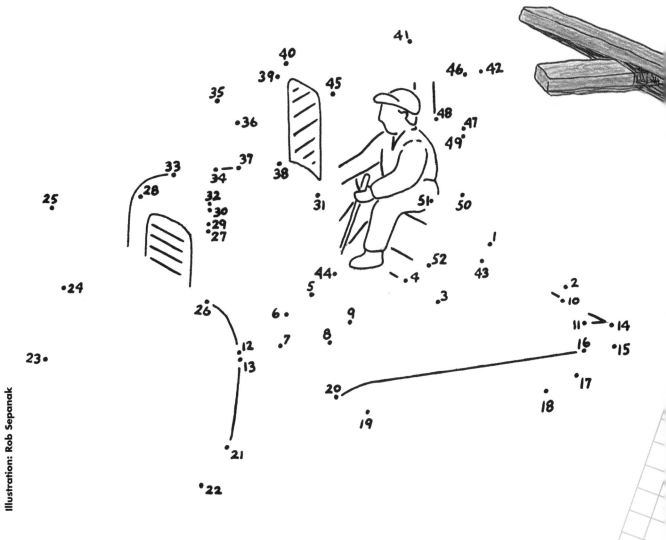

Illustration: Rob Sepanak

FEVER PITCH

Julie has been sick all week. She was supposed to keep a chart for the doctor, but forgot to enter all the numbers. She did make some notes, though. Can you use them to help her finish the chart?

Hint on page 46

Monday
Temperature: 100.4°
Pulse Rate (beats per minute): 100

Tuesday
Temp: 101.5°
Pulse: 90

Wednesday
Temp: 102.3°
Pulse: 86

Thursday
Temp: 101.1°
Pulse: 110

Friday
Temp: 100°
Pulse: 105

Saturday
Temp: 99.5°
Pulse: 99

Sunday
Temp: 98.6°
Pulse: 100

For her temperature, join the marks together in one line from left to right. Then do the same for her pulse rate. Please do your best, because she has to see the doctor in two hours.

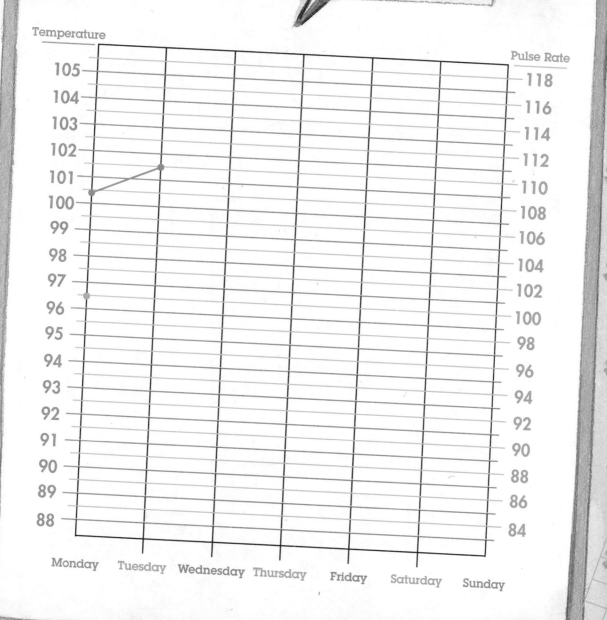

Temperature

						Pulse Rate
105 | | | | | | | 118
104 | | | | | | | 116
103 | | | | | | | 114
102 | | | | | | | 112
101 | | | | | | | 110
100 | | | | | | | 108
99 | | | | | | | 106
98 | | | | | | | 104
97 | | | | | | | 102
96 | | | | | | | 100
95 | | | | | | | 98
94 | | | | | | | 96
93 | | | | | | | 94
92 | | | | | | | 92
91 | | | | | | | 90
90 | | | | | | | 88
89 | | | | | | | 86
88 | | | | | | | 84

Monday   Tuesday   Wednesday   Thursday   Friday   Saturday   Sunday

Illustration: Anni Matsick

Answer on page 49

BUCKET BRIGADE

Each clown has a bucket of water. Look at the position of each bucket and match it to the silhouette that shows the correct amount of water inside.

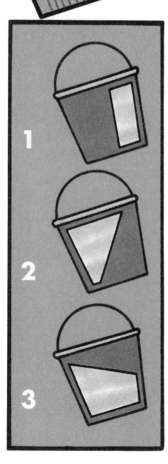

A

B

C

1
2
3

1
2
3

1
2
3

Hint on page 46

Illustration: R. Michael Palan

Answer on page 49

ANIMAL ADDITION

Can you find the value for each animal in the equations here? Each animal has a value from 1 to 9, and no two animals have the same value.

Illustration: David Helton

Hint on page 46

Answer on page 49

CUTTING A RUG

Becky Bangles, the ballerina, is furnishing a new bungalow. She wants to buy just enough carpet to cover the floors in each room.

6FT X 12FT

The carpet she likes comes in rolls of 6 feet by 12 feet. How many rolls will she need to cover all the rooms shown?

Hint on page 46

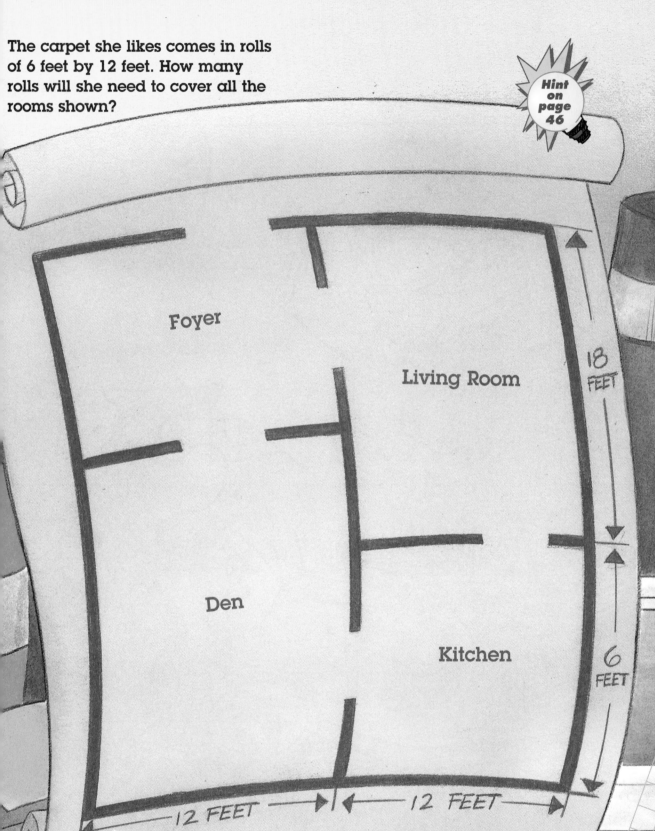

Foyer

Living Room

18 FEET

Den

Kitchen

6 FEET

12 FEET

12 FEET

Answer on page 49

DIGIT DOES IT

A crafty crook attempted to sneak out of the zoo with quite a snack. Luckily, Inspector Digit was visiting the zoo and is on the case.

He's already captured a coded message left in the gift shop. Can you decipher the note and find the fruit?

Hint on page 46

Illustration: John Nez

WHEN YOU'RE RIGHT

It's race day for the Wright Road Racers. The rules state that the racers must travel only in straight lines, and they can make only right-hand turns. They must touch each cone once. Can you find the right route for the Wrights to race?

START

FINIS

Illustration: Rick Geary

Answer on page 49

PARTIAL SUCCESS

You should be able to fill in bits and pieces of this puzzle by finding the words in the grid. Words are hidden across, up, or down, but not diagonally. Some letters will be used in more than one word. When you find all the words, write the leftover letters, from left to right and top to bottom, in the blanks to fill in the message.

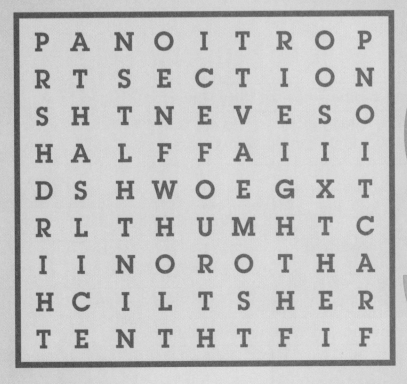

```
P A N O I T R O P
R T S E C T I O N
S H T N E V E S O
H A L F F A I I I
D S H W O E G X T
R L T H U M H T C
I I N O R O T H A
H C I L T S H E R
T E N T H T F I F
```

EIGHTH
FIFTH
FOURTH
FRACTION
HALF
MOST
NINTH

PORTION
SECTION
SEVENTH
SIXTH
SLICE
SOME
TENTH
THIRD

All of these words are only "some" because they

are __ __ __ __ __ __ of __ __ __ __ __ __ __.

Answer on page 49

ROUND ABOUT

Can you tell when each event pictured here took place? You don't always need to be exact. Just pick one of the three choices,

1. Man walked on the moon.

1945	Before	After
$2 \times 2 = 5$	$2 \times 2 = 2$	$2 \times 2 = 4$

2. The Wright brothers flew at Kitty Hawk.

1933	Before	After
$6 \times 3 = 17$	$6 \times 3 = 18$	$6 \times 3 = 19$

3. Marco Polo traveled to China.

1271	Before	After
$28 \div 4 = 7$	$28 \div 4 = 8$	$28 \div 4 = 6$

4. The electric sewing machine was developed.

1800	Before	After
$35 \div 5 = 5$	$35 \div 5 = 6$	$35 \div 5 = 7$

5. America declared independence from Englan

1776	Before	After
$4 \times 9 = 36$	$4 \times 9 = 37$	$4 \times 9 = 38$

6. Air conditioning was developed.

1960	Before	After
$12 \times 2 = 22$	$12 \times 3 = 36$	$12 \times 4 = 46$

and you should round up the answers in no time. The equation with the correct answer will give you the right date.

7. Francis Drake began his travels around the globe.

1400	Before	After
48 ÷ 4 = 11	46 ÷ 4 = 11	44 ÷ 4 = 11

8. King Tut ruled Egypt.

1743	Before	After
49 ÷ 7 = 6	49 ÷ 7 = 7	49 ÷ 7 = 8

9. Gold was discovered in California.

1510	Before	After
18 - 17 = 2	18 + 17 = 32	18 × 17 = 306

10. George Washington became the first President of the United States.

1832	Before	After
6 ÷ 3 = 3	6 × 3 = 18	6 + 3 = 10

11. First United States radio broadcast took place.

1957	Before	After
38 +19 = 47	38 - 19 = 19	38 ÷ 19 = 3

12. *Titanic* sank.

1912	Before	After
5 × 5 = 25	5 + 5 = 15	5 - 5 = 1

Answer on page 49

Illustration: Rocky Fuller

LIBRARY LAUGHS

Answer on page 49

Dewey has some funny books in his library. To check one out, you've got to solve each problem. Then go to the shelves to find the volume with the number that matches each answer. Put the matching letter in the blank beside each answer. Read down the letters you've filled in to find the title and author of the book Dewey just finished reading.

Shelf labels:
- U 21, N 14, V 22, K 11
- F 6, J, W 23, A 1, B 2, C 3, D 4, E 5, P 16, Q 17, R 18, S 19, T 20
- L 12, M 13, Y 25, G 7, H 8, X 24
- Z 26, O 15, 9

Illustration: Scott Peck

Hint on page 47

Problems:

$2 \times 3 =$ ___
$16 + 5 =$ ___
$28 \div 2 =$ ___
$28 - 5 =$ ___
$3 \times 3 =$ ___
$14 + 6 =$ ___
$24 \div 3 =$ ___
$19 - 5 =$ ___
$3 \times 7 =$ ___
$9 + 4 =$ ___
$4 \div 2 =$ ___
$9 - 4 =$ ___
$6 \times 3 =$ ___
$13 + 6 =$ ___
$8 - 6 =$ ___
$5 \times 5 =$ ___
$7 + 3 =$ ___
$42 \div 2 =$ ___
$11 - 10 =$ ___
$2 \times 7 =$ ___
$4 \times 5 =$ ___
$8 + 7 =$ ___
$45 \div 3 =$ ___
$24 - 4 =$ ___
$8 \times 1 =$ ___
$11 + 7 =$ ___
$25 \div 5 =$ ___
$15 - 10 =$ ___

STACKING STANLEY

Hint on page 47

Last week, Stan stacked all his cardboard. This week, he's stacking all the money he received from the recycling center. Can you tell how much money Stan already stacked?

50¢ PENNIES

50¢ PENNIES

$5 DIMES

$5 DIMES

$5 DIMES

$2 NICKELS

$2 NICKELS

$2 NICKELS

$10 QUARTERS

$10 QUARTERS

Illustration: R. Michael Palan

Answer on page 50

SCRAMBLED PICTURE

Copy these mixed-up wedges into the spaces on the next page to unscramble the scene. The letters and numbers tell you where each wedge belongs.

A3

B5

B2

B6

B3

B1

A5

B4

A1

A4

A2

A6

We've done the first one, A3,
to start you off.

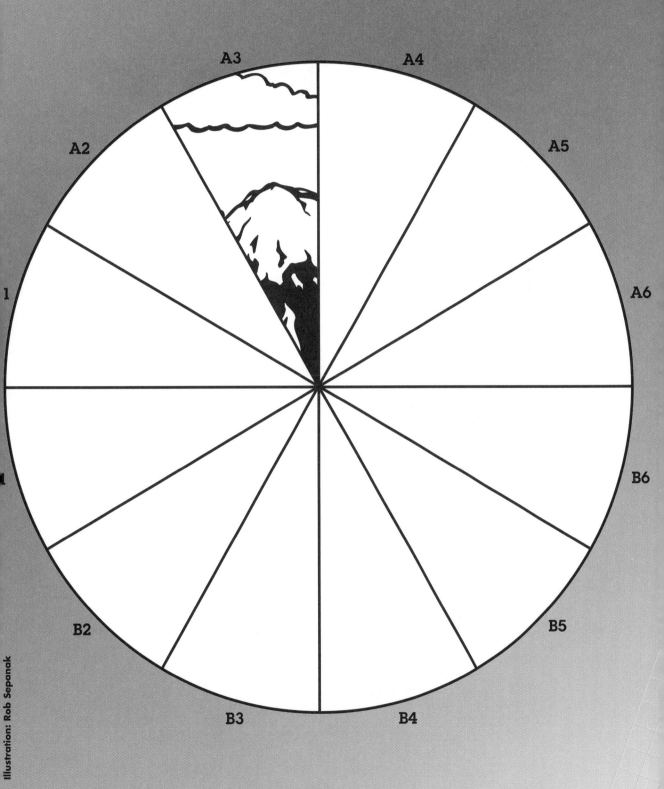

A3   A4

A2   A5

1   A6

A2   B6

B2   B5

B2   B3   B4

Illustration: Rob Sepanak

Answer on page 50

READ ALL ABOUT IT

These numbers can be found in almost any newspaper. Can you tell which section these numbers were pulled from?

Answer on page 50

PEN PALS

Francine is trying to raise some chickens for a 4-H project. She needs to enclose each rooster with three different hens. She has enough material to make only two straight fences across the pen. Can you help her place the two fences so that she'll have four pens, each with one rooster and three hens?

Illustration: David Helton

Answer on page 50

Hint on page 47

SCHEDULING PROBLEMS

Stacey and Stephen have so much to do that they need a calendar to help them remember

STEPHEN

Acting class on Wednesdays at 3:30 p.m.
Tae kwon do on Tuesdays at 5:00 p.m.
Invited to Tad's birthday party—1:00 p.m. on the 8th
Volleyball practice every weekday at 11:30 a.m.
Bike trip from the 1st to the 3rd
Mow the lawn on the first and third Fridays
Boy Scouts on second and fourth Friday of each month—
    7:00 p.m.

STACEY

Violin lessons every Tuesday at 2:30 p.m.
Dentist appointment—10:00 a.m. on the 22nd
Girl Scout meetings on Monday nights—7:30 p.m.
Recital on the 19th
Softball practice every Saturday at 4:00 p.m.
Sleepover at Greta's—the 28th
Choral group—Sundays at 2:30 p.m.

everything. Can you fill in this
calendar to help them keep track
of their activities this month?

SUNDAY	MONDAY	TUESDAY	WEDNESDAY	THURSDAY	FRIDAY	SATURDAY
				1	2	3
4	5	6	7	8	9	10
11	12	13	14	15	16	17
18	19	20	21	22	23	24
25	26	27	28	29	30	31

Answer on page 50

175 SQUARE

Place each number from 1 to 20 into the empty boxes on this grid so that the numbers in each row across and down, and the two main diagonals, will add up to 175.

22		30		38	21	46
47	23		31		39	
	48	24		32		40
41		49	25		33	
	42		43	26		34
35		36		44	27	
	29		37		45	28

Hint on page 47

BOX SCORES

The eleventh letter: ___
The twelfth letter: ___
The fourth letter: ___
The nineteenth letter: ___
The fifteenth letter: ___
The thirteenth letter: ___
The tenth letter: ___
The first letter: ___
The eleventh letter: ___
The nineteenth letter: ___
The eighth letter: ___
The twelfth letter: ___
The seventeenth letter: ___
The eighteenth letter: ___
The third letter: ___
The twelfth letter: ___
The ninth letter: ___
The sixteenth letter: ___
The fourteenth letter: ___
The seventh letter: ___
The tenth letter: ___
The first letter: ___
The eleventh letter: ___
The seventh letter: ___
The first letter: ___
The thirteenth letter: ___
The seventh letter: ___
The eighteenth letter: ___
The tenth letter: ___
The twelfth letter: ___
The fifteenth letter: ___
The first letter: ___
The nineteenth letter: ___
The sixteenth letter: ___

Look at the impressive title just awarded to manager Doug Owtt of the Shelbyville Isotopes. Using only the letters in Doug's new title, write the requested letters on the scoreboard. If you read the letters from top to bottom, you'll learn something else about Big Doug.

TRULY POLISHED MANAGER

Answer on page 50

33

CROSSNUMBER

Answer each question as you would in a regular crossword, and then place the numbers into the grid, one number per box.

ACROSS

1. $\frac{1}{4}$ of $5.00 equals this many pennies
3. As easy as ___ , ___ , ___
5. Number of days in a "leap year" February
6. _____ Arabian Nights
8. "Sweet" teen birthday age
9. Another way to write 37 minutes before 6:00
11. 120 months equals this many years
12. . . . 6, 5, 4, ___ , ___ , ___ , ___
14. Number of yards in 60 feet
15. Three-digit phone number for emergencies
16. November first, written out numerically

DOWN

2. Number of years in a bicentennial
3. The last teen year
4. Number of days in a leap year
5. 10,615 × 2
7. Translation of these two numbers from Spanish: cero, cinco
10. Number of ounces in 2 pounds
11. Translation of these three roman numerals: I, V, IX
13. Another way to write 11 minutes after 1:00
14. The year 2001 begins the ___ st century

Hint on page 47

Answer on page 50

Illustration: Rick Geary

35

MATHMAGIC

The Great Numero

Let's address a new trick.

Ask someone to write down her house number. Don't let the person show it to you, but ask for the number of digits in the address.

Have her double the number she wrote down.

Now ask her to add 3 to the number.

Tell her to multiply the number by 50.

Now have her add 100 to the new number.

When she gives you the result, you should then be able to give her the number of her house.

Answer on page 50

PRECISE ICE

A true champion will be able to skate over this complete figure without going back over or crossing any lines.

Illustration: Barbara Gray

Answer on page 50

STOCK PILE

```
.....2.53...41 5/8.....
.RBR....+7.32.....
.-4....TNY....-11.14
....ZRL..-4.56.....
.....NAV..+24......
TRQL...-7.42...5.4///
```

1. Della bought 1 share each of stocks 1, 3, 5, and 7.

2. Filbert bought 1 share each of stocks 1, 5, 8, and 10.

3. Allie bought 1 share each of stocks 4, 6, 7, and 10.

4. Willy bought 1 share each of stocks 2, 5, 7, and 9.

5. Millie bought 1 share each of stocks 1, 2, 9, and 10.

6. Wally bought 1 share each of stocks 3, 4, 7, and 8.

Who made the most profit by the closing bell on Friday? Who had lost the most money?

Illustration: Scott Peck

To figure out if a stock lost or made money, find the difference in price from Monday to Friday. For example, if you bought a share of stock in Buzzo's Windup Bees for $.55, and sold it on Friday for $.40, that stock lost $.15 for the week.

Stock	Monday	Friday's close	Gain/Loss
1. Buzzo's Windup Bees	$.55	$.40	-$.15
2. Bloomin' Flowers	.60	.63	_____
3. Twinkletoe Ballet Shoes	1.00	.84	_____
4. Smudgy Ink Co.	.90	.76	_____
5. Buncha Bananas	.50	.62	_____
6. Zippy Skates	.80	.74	_____
7. Floataway Boats	2.00	2.28	_____
8. Round and Round Rugs	1.50	1.42	_____
9. Squeaky Balloons	.75	1.10	_____
10. Loopy Laces	.30	.28	_____

Hint on page 47

Answer on page 50

TRUE OR FALSE

What is the "definition" of antidotes?

You'll find another of our funny definitions by solving the equations here. If our answer is correct, write the letter from the True column in the blank. If our answer is wrong, write the letter from the False column in the blank. When you're done, read down the letters you wrote to find the definition.

	True	False	Letter
$1 \times 2 = 2$	W	T	____
$3 + 4 = 5$	I	H	____
$6 - 5 = 3$	M	A	____
$8 \times 7 = 56$	T	E	____
$9 + 10 = 19$	M	I	____
$11 \times 4 = 41$	S	Y	____
$12 \div 3 = 4$	U	O	____
$13 - 2 = 11$	N	F	____
$14 + 12 = 25$	T	C	____
$15 \div 5 = 10$	H	L	____
$16 \times 1 = 17$	E	E	____
$17 - 1 = 16$	S	E	____
$18 \div 3 = 6$	W	S	____
$19 - 13 = 6$	I	S	____
$20 \div 10 = 10$	E	F	____
$21 + 17 = 38$	E	N	____
$22 \times 3 = 60$	C	D	____
$23 - 19 = 5$	E	O	____
$24 \div 4 = 6$	E	N	____
$25 \div 5 = 5$	S	O	____

Hint on page 47

Answer on page 51

COLOR BY NUMBERS

Use the key to color in the spaces.

1 dot — White	4 dots — Gray
2 dots — Brown	5 dots — Green
3 dots — Black	6 dots — Blue

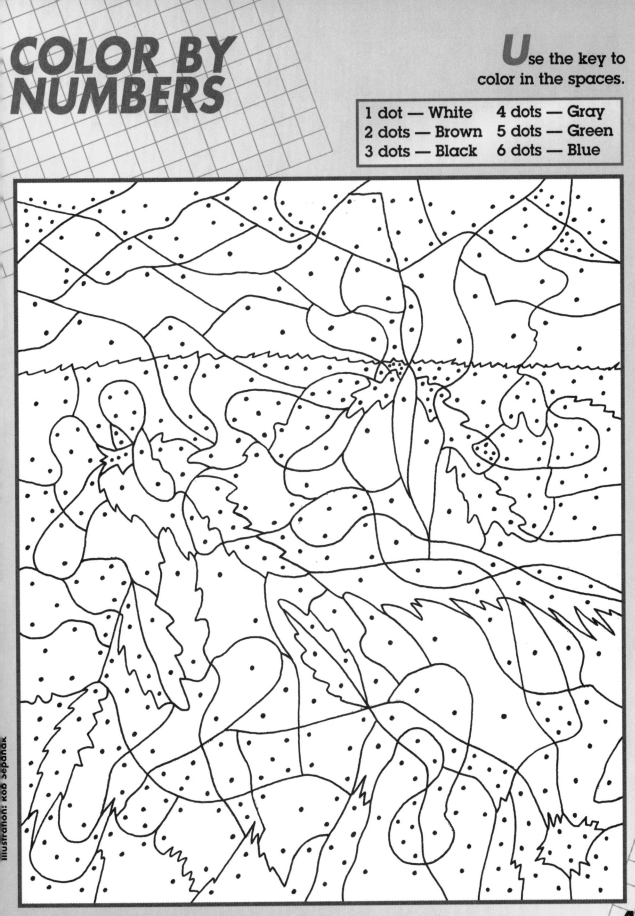

Illustration: Rob Sepanak

Answer on page 51

MAP MOVES

Follow the directions to travel around this map and collect each letter you land on. Do not collect

- Start at the house and travel 4 squares north.
- Now go 5 squares east.
- Then go northwest 4 squares.
- Turn south 1.
- Travel 4 squares southeast and then 2 squares southwest.
- Climb 2 squares northwest to the mountain.
- Now climb down south 1.
- Go southeast 2 and then east 3.
- Head north to 1 square past the river.
- Go north 1 more.
- Turn and move southwest 4.
- Turn again and go northwest 2.
- Go east 1 square past the tree.
- Go south to the bush.
- Move southwest 1 square.
- Now cut southeast 1 square.
- Travel west 3.
- Go north as far as you can.
- Turn east for 3 squares.

What can turn without moving?

_ _ _ _ _ : _ _ _ _ _ _ _ _ _ _ _ _ _.

Hint on page 47

42   *MATHMANIA*

letters you just pass over. When you finish, the collected letters will spell out the answer to the riddle.

Illustration: Michael Austin

LONG SHOT

Write the answer to each statement in the blank circle beside it. Find the matching answer in the column on the right. Then use a ruler to draw a straight line to and from the matching numbers. Each line will go through one letter on a shoe box. Copy those letters onto the spaces, keeping them in the same order as the questions they go with. You'll find the answer to today's question in no time.

Hint on page 47

How long is a shoe?

 $\overline{1}$ $\overline{2}$ $\overline{3}$ $\overline{4}$ $\overline{5}$ $\overline{6}$ $\overline{7}$ $\overline{8}$ $\overline{9}$

1. Number of inches in a yard: ◯

2. Number of inches in a foot: ◯

3. Number of feet in a yard: ◯

4. Number of feet in a mile: ◯

5. Number of feet in a half-mile: ◯

6. Number of feet in a fathom: ◯

7. Number of centimeters in a meter: ◯

8. Number of kilometers in 10 miles: ◯

9. Number of miles usually run in a marathon: ◯

Answer on page 51

5,280

6

16.1

36

100

12

26.2

2,640

3

A O L F N T O G O

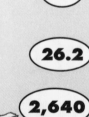

Illustration: Don Robison

STATE THE NUMBERS

Can you answer these questions about the United States of America?

1. What's the fewest letters in the name of any state? What's the most letters?

2. How many state names begin with the letter A? Of these, how many also end with the letter A?

3. Which letter begins the most state names?

4. How many letters do not begin the names of any states? How many letters do not appear in any state names?

5. Are there more states to the east or to the west of the Mississippi River?

Hint on page 47

Answer on page 51

MATHMANIA **45**

HINTS AND BRIGHT IDEAS

These hints may help with some of the trickier puzzles.

STARTING LINEUP (page 3)
The players with the highest and lowest numbers are not in the starting lineup.

RIDDLE SQUARES (page 6)
ABC is not linked with number 1. There are 4 quarts in 1 gallon and 16 ounces in 1 pound.

FINISH BY 5 (page 7)
Follow this path: 5, 10, 15, 20, 25, 30, 35, 40.

CLOCK WATCHER (pages 8-9)
Each clock has a tag with a letter. That letter should go in the empty space above the matching time.

SPLIT DECISIONS (page 10)
The bottom number, or denominator, of the fraction is the same as the number of pieces in each cake.

FEVER PITCH (pages 12-13)
Find the place on each chart where the numbers in Julie's notes would fall. Draw a dot over the right day.

BUCKET BRIGADE (page 14)
Look at how the buckets are tipped. Try to imagine the point at which the water would splash out.

ANIMAL ADDITION (page 15)
Frog has the highest value. Rabbit has the lowest.

CUTTING A RUG (pages 16-17)
Each roll of carpet covers 6 by 12 feet, or 72 square feet. How many square feet are in the rooms?

DIGIT DOES IT (pages 18-19)
The word *Inspector* appears in the note's greeting. Use the coded numbers in this word to help figure out the rest of the message.

LIBRARY LAUGHS (page 24)
Remember to consult the books to find
the letter that matches each number.

STACKING STANLEY (page 25)
Figure out how much money is in each roll of coins.
Then multiply by the number of rolls for each denomination.
Add your four totals together.

PEN PALS (page 29)
The two fences will cross at one point.

175 SQUARE (page 32)
The top row across has spaces for two numbers. The total
of the top row is 157. That leaves 18. 5 + 13 = 18. Place those
numbers in that order from left to right. The number 4 goes
in the lower left. Look for sequencing in the diagonal spaces.

CROSSNUMBER (pages 34-35)
There are 16 ounces in a pound, 12 months in a year,
1001 Arabian Nights, and 200 years in a bicentennial.

STOCK PILE (pages 38-39)
First figure out all the gains and losses for the stocks. Then
look at the individual shares owned by the different buyers.

TRUE OR FALSE (page 40)
If you have problems with the math, look at the words
that are being formed. Which letters help make
complete words?

MAP MOVES (pages 42-43)
You may have to go over or move around some objects.

LONG SHOT (page 44)
A mile gets the largest number. A yard gets the
smallest. A fathom is 6 feet.

STATE THE NUMBERS (page 45)
Only one letter doesn't appear in a state name.
Which one might it be?

ANSWERS

COVER
pea
penny
quarter
orange
coconut
soccer ball
car tire
moon
sun

STARTING LINEUP (page 3)
9 + 10 + 18 + 25 + 38 = 100

COUNT ON LIZ (pages 4-5)

RIDDLE SQUARES (page 6)
1. What breaks without falling?
   DAY
2. What falls without breaking?
   NIGHT

FINISH BY 5 (page 7)

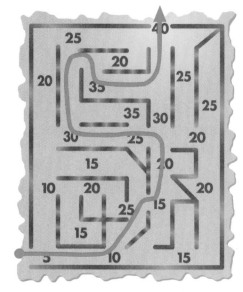

CLOCK WATCHER (pages 8-9)
1. What time is everyone's favorite?
   TIME OFF

2. How do you know when a clock is embarrassed?
   IT HIDES ITS FACE BEHIND ITS HANDS.

SPLIT DECISIONS (page 10)

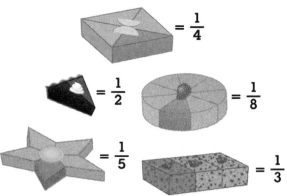

DOTS A LOT (page 11)

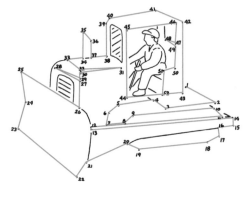